C

MW00885898

PLC Logics and HMI screens

for

4-20 mA Sensors Automation

A pratical approach to quantities measurement and monitoring
using IEC 61131 - 3 Ladder Logic

AUTOMATION RECIPES - VOLUME 2

Rosario Cirrito

Copyright

Synopsis

This booklet is the second of a series dedicated to automation recipes created with the PLC (Programmable Logic Controller) and HMI (Human Machine Interface) binomial. The series is aimed at an audience of readers with an elementary knowledge of PLC programming, eager to learn advanced solutions, extensively tested on real systems.

In modern computer programming, generally oriented to the development of "object-oriented" software, the developer strives, as much as possible, to resort to so-called "Design Patterns", standard solutions for frequently recurring problems. A design pattern describes a problem, particularly recurring in a given context, and then provide the heart of the solution to this problem. It is therefore possible to successfully reuse this solution, thousands and thousands of times, with the certainty of using an efficient and well-tested solution.

In the present series, which deals exclusively with development on PLC-HMI, the term "design pattern" has been replaced by the term "automation recipe" for an easier understanding by the non IT reader.

In the chapters of this book we will show in detail an automation recipe that can be reused in any PLC-HMI automation project that uses "electric motors". The recipe has also been optimized for operation with Scada supervision systems.

This second book illustrates the automation recipe for measuring and monitoring quantities acquired with 4-20 mA current sensors.

In detail, the first section, dedicated to the application domain, analyzes the various types of measurement used to acquire physical quantities such as pressure, level, flow, electric current and temperature.

The second section deals with the development of combined software for both PLC and HMI. The logic of the two function blocks (UDFB), Conv4_20mA and AnalogSts are analyzed. The first block shows how to convert from analog 4-20 mA to engineering quantities, while the second one explains how to monitor the status of the analog signal based on preset parameters such as set-point, hysteresis, dead band, operational thresholds and first and second level alarms. For both functional blocks are developed in detail the relevant screens for displaying the values, the local monitoring of the states and the setting of adjustment parameters. In addition to the logic of the function blocks, two auxiliary subroutines are also discussed, VirtualAI and Init, to be called only once (singleton) in the main program.

The third section shows, finally, the application of the concepts, developed in the previous chapters, to a concrete case of level control in a waste water pumping station.

The HMI solutions have been extensively tested on the OCS, Operator Control System, manufactured by Horner Apg. OCS combines a Controller, Operator Interface, Network and I/O into a single product. While the author, has been widely using Siemens, Allen Bradley, GE Fanuc PLCs he has focused the books of this series on the Horner OCSs because Horner provides Cscape, an integrated development environment, extremely easy to use and above all completely free.

All the logics, published in the book, have been developed using the IEC61131-3 compliant Ladder language; therefore it is extremely easy to migrate them on almost all the PLCs of other manufacturers.

The same applies to HMI screens whose graphic controls are very similar on the different equipment offered on the market.

The reader who already has experience with other manufacturers' equipment can therefore continue to use what he knows best.

Contents

1.1 The analog sensors

The field level

The lower layer in the pyramidal architecture of a control system consists of the level occupied by the process and that is the so-called "field level". The functions of this logical layer are essentially two:

a) receive information from the process (input function) using special devices called sensors;

b) implement command directives against the process (output function) by means of devices called actuators.

The distinguishing feature of a process control system is in fact its ability to:

1) interrogate the sensors in the field;

2) converting the electrical signals generated by the latter into engineering quantities such as pressures, levels and temperatures;

3) start the appropriate command or control actions on the actuators envisaged by the management strategies, identified during the project and stored in the PLC application program.

The direction of the electrical signals is always expressed from the point of view of the control system, so any signal from any source addressed to the controller is considered an input; similarly, any signal that is addressed to the contactors or to the system machinery is considered an output from the controller.

Definitions

Let's now look at some important definitions. We can define measurement a set of operations with the aim of determining the value of a quantity.

The signal is defined, as the physical variable of which one or more parameters contain information of one or more variables that the signal represents. The input signal is the signal applied to the input of a device, element or system. The output signal is the signal provided by a device, element or system.

The digital signal is the signal whose information parameter can not assume any value outside a set of discrete values represented by integers. The quantization process, which characterizes it, is that by which the field of a variable is divided into a finite number of distinct subfields, each of which is represented by an assigned value called quantized value.

The binary signal (binary signal) is a quantized signal having only 2 possible values.

The analog signal (analog signal) is the signal whose information parameter can assume all the values within a given field.

The analogue signal is indispensable for measuring process quantities such as pressures, temperatures, flow rates, levels, etc., characterized by varying over time with continuity within a more or less extensive measuring range. The instrumentation to collect this information from the process is made up of components such as sensors, transducers and transmitters.

The sensor is the element that converts physical quantities into a measurable signal according to a specific physical law. Downstream of the sensor, the transducer converts this physical signal into an electrical output variable that a suitable amplifier converts into an electrical signal, in DC current or voltage, normalized.

Sensor, translator and amplifier, incorporated in a single device, form the classic transmitter, that is a measuring instrument with an output signal normalized in the fields: 4-20 mA (preferential signal compared to 0-20 mA); 1-5 V, 0-5 V, 0-10 V, -10 / + 10 V.

The variation of the output signal is linearly proportional to that of the measured variable.

The DC current signal, being scarcely influenced by external electromagnetic fields, is widely used in the industrial field for remote connections, even greater than a few hundred meters, towards the various measurement points of the process; direct voltage signal is generally limited to panel or back panel devices or in the environments, not too disturbed, from an electromagnetic point of view, such as those of residential or civil applications.

The direct current signal is therefore always preferable to the direct voltage signal since it is not affected by the length of the connection line and by the voltage drop caused by the electrical resistance of the relative cables; it is also not affected by the input impedance of the receiver instrument in a sufficiently high variation range.

The 4-20 mA direct current signal, also called "live zero", is also to be preferred to the 0-20 mA signal, called "true zero" for a series of reasons. The main one is that it allows to discriminate between the null value signal, to which in any case it corresponds a current even if minimum of 4 mA, from that of interrupted cable which obviously corresponds a current of 0 mA. Its typical connection is two-wire so that the transmitter is powered by the same two signal transmission-reception wires and therefore it is possible to supply several receivers connected in series in the same measuring ring (for example a local recorder in addition to the PLC).

The 0-20 mA signal, on the other hand, always requires a 3-wire connection, which is also used by those 4-20 mA transmitters which require a minimum supply current of more than 4 mA for correct operation. In this case the power cable is different from the signal cable while the third cable is common both for the power supply and for the signal.

The power supply of the measuring ring must supply a continuous voltage between 20 and 30 V while the transmitter must be able to drive a load impedance of the user device between 0 and 300 ohms; typical values for a transmitter are 600 ohms and 24 V that allow us to connect up to two receivers in the same measuring ring. The receiver instrument, in turn, can autonomously convert the normalized signal into current directly into a voltage signal through the interposition in series of a resistor with a nominal value of 250 ohms and a tolerance of 0.1% or better 0.05%. In this case, it is necessary to condition the 4-20 mA signal through a 250 ohm drop resistor in a 1-5 V signal, as shown in Figure 1.1.1. This voltage signal can, in turn, be sent to several receivers in parallel, provided that they obviously have an input impedance significantly higher than 250 ohms of the shunt resistor.

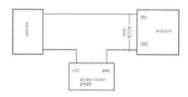

2.1 The modular programming and the memory mapping

The types of languages provided by the IEC 61131-3 standard can be considered as low-medium level programming languages.

This standard was developed to ensure a certain portability of the programs between PLCs from different suppliers.

Its greatest merit consists in being oriented to the modular development of control applications thus allowing the overall logic to be divided into subroutines recalled cyclically by a single main program.

The individual subroutines can in turn recall standard functional blocks provided by the language or even functional blocks UDFB, acronym of User Defined Function Block, expressly developed by the user.

A function block groups an algorithm and a set of private data so it is parameterized with reference to the input and output variables; this allows the developer to create multiple instances of each block belonging to the same automation system.

We will develop this important concept in greater detail in the following paragraphs.

To program subprograms and function blocks, the standard allows the developer to use one of the following five languages:

1)Ladder Diagram (LD)
2)Instruction List (IL)
3)Function Block Diagram (FBD)
4)Structured Text (ST)
5)Sequential Function Chart (SFC)

The choice is dictated by personal preferences or by the specific professional background of the programmer.

The modular decomposition of the application is clearly visible in Figure 2.1.1 which shows the structure of the various components typical of a project realized with the Horner CScape development environment.

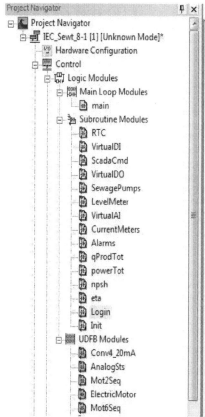

The control logic is therefore contained in a series of "Logic Modules". In summary, at the top of the hierarchy of modules we have the Main Loop Modules that contain at least one main main module, which runs cyclically. The main program calls in sequence, one at a time, the various "Subroutine Modules" which in turn can recall the functional blocks several times, but with different parameters each time. The latter can be both the standard function blocks, already provided by the language for the general purpose logical instructions, or the specific user-defined blocks, the "UDFB Modules".

The PLC control logic as well as the HMI display logic is however developed on a PC, almost exclusively in the Windows environment. The relevant source file is saved, periodically and after complete modifications, on the PC hard disk.

Whatever the hardware being used, PC or PLC, a set of RAM working memories is always needed both to store the program instructions and to save, at each scan cycle, the data of the dynamic variables. Today's PC generally has a RAM of 4-8 GBytes, while the PLC requires far more modest memories, from 256 kB to 1MB, to store control logic of even particularly complex systems, as well as a few thousand internal variables.

High-level PC languages use Short, Byte, Integer, Long, Float, Double primitive variables that occupy from 8 to 64 bits of memory; the data type most frequently used by the PLC is instead the Word, composed of 16 bits, also called register (% R). A single Word or Register, having 16 bits in total, thanks to the binary numbering system, can represent Integers with a sign between -32768 and + 32767 or without sign in the range 0 and 65365.

When it is necessary to represent integers of higher value or real number, a 32-bit representation is used, obtained by merging two adjacent 16-bit registers.

A 16-bit register can also be used to aggregate the binary state of logical bits, each of which occupies one bit, in groups of 16. This packed solution is particularly compact and efficient especially when these variables are transmitted to Scada systems or transferred on the network from one PLC to another.

The individual bits of the Boolean variables then become individually accessible at address% Rx.y with x, index of the register, and y index of the bit, between 1 and 16: so %R1.5 will indicate the bit 5 of the register 1. Boolean binary values can in any case be stored also as retentive variables of type% M or non-retentive of type% T.

In addition to storing integers, real numbers and packed bits, the% R registers are also used to store enumerations of machine and sensor states that can be associated with predefined text strings in the HMI interface screens. We will show such use when we take care of displaying dynamic texts in the HMI panel.

A memory representation of a physical quantity, acquired in real time, is, for example, a pressure that at a certain moment takes on a value equal to 8.95 bar. In this case we can represent it as a 32 bit real value, using two consecutive registers, for example %R201 and %R202; or as an integer value, equal to 895, with occupation of a single 16-bit register, for example% R200. This second mode allows us to store the actual data in half the memory space, which is especially important when the data must be sent to a supervision system or another controller along a serial line that is not too fast; but this approach has the drawback that the correct representation of the displayed format must always be managed, by PLC logic and HMI configuration, keeping in mind how many decimal digits are to be taken into account. An example of a register containing an enumeration of dynamic texts is constituted by the status register of a pump whose value can vary, in real time, within a certain set of logic precoded states stored in tabular form within the HMI device, as shown in figure 2.1.2.

Value	Text
0	???
1	ON
3	ON_SEL
4	OFF
6	REM_0
6	LOC_0
18	ALARM
32	INIBIT
64	INTERD
130	FDBACK

The integers shown in the Value column correspond to the logical states shown in the Text column. The latter can therefore be displayed in a text field inside the graphic pages of the operator panel associated with the PLC.

2.2 The Conv4_20mA function block

Problem

The analogue signal processing software is required to perform a reverse conversion, with respect to that made by the sensors, ie, from an electrical measure to an engineering measure. We have available either the variable value of the analog input or the% R memory register on which it has been transiently stored in addition to the fixed parameters of the transmitter working range.

Solution

The design pattern control logic is contained in the UDFB module named Conv4_20mA. The function block will be called, in the main program, a number of times equal to the number of transmitters to be acquired.

Map of local variables

The figure 3.15.1 displays the table of input, output and internal variables:

Name	Type	Dim	Attrib.
⊟ 🔲 Conv4_20mA			
iX0	INT		IN
iX1	INT		IN
iY0	INT		IN
iY1	INT		IN
iX	INT		IN
iY	INT		OUT
rX0	REAL		
rX1	REAL		
rY0	REAL		
rY1	REAL		
rX	REAL		
rY	REAL		
mNum	REAL		
mDen	REAL		
xDif	REAL		

The iX0-iX1 parameters are the start and end values of the controller's ADC converter range, for example, 0-32767.

The parameters iY0-iY1 are the start and end values of the transmitter, reported on an entire basis, for example in the case of a measuring range between 0.00 and 25.00 bar, iY0 will be equal to 0 and iY1 = 2500; the number of decimals required is incorporated.

The iX value is the value provided in real time by the ADC converter of the analog input module. In output, the UDFB module will supply the iY value containing the engineering value expressed on an integer basis.

The logic

In the example, the calling program requires the conversion of the value stored in the 16-bit register APRead for a pressure probe operating in the 0-25 bar range. Since we want to proceed with two significant digits, we will enter the values 0 and 2500 respectively in the input parameters iY0 and iY1. We will supply 0 and 32767 as the values of iX0 and iX1 and we will get the output in real time APValue which gives us the instantaneous pressure expressed as an integer value, in absolute value, with two decimal digits. An example of an APConv instance, referred to by the main module for measuring high pressure on a refrigeration system, is shown in Figure 3.15.2:

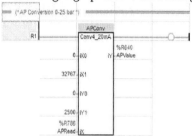

The first five rungs of the Conv4_20mA function block repeatedly call the standard function block of the ANY_TO_REAL language to transform a 16-bit integer register into a real 32-bit register, as shown in figure 3.15.3. The R1 - R5 rungs transform the integer values iX0, iX1, iY0, iY1 and iXin in real values to not lose accuracy in subsequent algebraic operations.

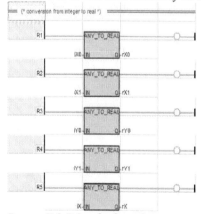

Rungs R6-R8 calculate the numerator mNum and the denominator mDen of the linear interpolation formula as well as the intermediate variable xDif, as shown in figure 3.15.4.

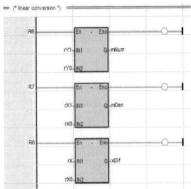

The R9-R11 rungs calculate the intermediate variable rY and finally the final line R12 provides the 16-bit integer value of the iY parameter, as shown in figure 3.15.5.

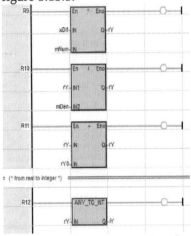

It is necessary to pay attention that, probably for historical reasons related to the need to compact the data in memory, the physical quantities that would normally be represented as real values (32-bit) are often stored as integer variables (16-bit). Thus operating, a memory space economy of 50% is achieved but in this way the developer must constantly keep in mind the number of decimal digits, in order to ensure a correct display both on the HMI devices and on the Scada system.

2.3 The Conv4_20mA Human Machine Interface

To display a measured quantity, we use the Numeric Data graphical control. Figure 2.3.1 shows a practical example: the PressureValue value is displayed in the graphic page SYSTEM which offers a synoptic representation of a booster pump system.

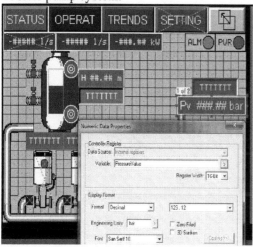

The configuration of the Numeric Data control is shown at the bottom right. It is necessary to define a numeric field in the dialog box as shown in the figure indicating the variable (PressureValue), its display format (Decimal 123.12) and avoiding to enable the Edit / Write checkbox since the type of variable, being a measure, is a read-only type.

2.4 The AnalogSts function block

Problem

When the measured quantity must also be controlled, the functional block UDFB is used: AnalogSts.

The international standard IEC 902 introduces precise definitions when the process variable, as well as measured, must also be controlled - regulated around a reference value.

VD desired variable (set-point) is the value of the requested variable while the measured variable VM (measured variable) is the variable measured by the transmitter and sent to the controller; Off-set deviation is the steady deviation between the desired variable and the measured variable.

Output variable or manipulated variable m (output variable - manipulated variable) is the variable or correction signal sent by the regulator to the final regulating organ.

Proportional action P (proportional action) is the type of control action in which the variations of the output variables are proportional to the variations of the input variable; integral action I (integral action) is the type of control action in which the variations in time (derivative in time) of the output variable are proportional to the variations of the input variable while the derivative action D (derivative action) is the type of action control system in which the value of the output variable is proportional to the derivative over time of the input variable.

Proportional + integral action + PID derivative (PID action) is the type of control action in which the output is proportional to a linear combination of the input (action P), its integral (action I) and its derivative (action D).

Two steps action (two steps action) is the type of action in which the output can take two different values; switching value for a step-action element is each value of the input variable for which the output variable changes while the hysteresis zone (differential gap) is the difference between the upper and lower switching value.

All-or-nothing action (on-off action) is a two-step action in which one of the output values is zero.

In the regulation, our goal is that the measured variable is kept close to a desired value, pre-set during the project and possibly reassigned via the HMI interface during the system conduction phase.

The purpose of the AnalogSts functional block is not so much to provide a direct control action of the plant's machinery as to provide the appropriate indications to a subsequent control strategy, of a higher level, based on the actual type of controlled plant.

Local variables map

Figure 4.7.1 displays the table of input, output and internal variables of the block.

Name	Type	Dim.	Attrib.
⊟ 🗊 AnalogSts			
LowReas	INT		IN
HighReas	INT		IN
EngValue	INT		IN
SetPoint	INT		IN
Hysteresis	INT		IN
DeadBand	INT		IN
LowAlarm	INT		IN
HighAlarm	INT		IN
AnalogSts	INT		OUT
fOk	BOOL		OUT
fLowOp	BOOL		OUT
fHighOp	BOOL		OUT
fLowAlm	BOOL		OUT
fHighAlm	BOOL		OUT
AnalogErr	BOOL		OUT
HighOper	INT		OUT
LowOper	INT		OUT
LowDB	INT		
HighDB	INT		
LoAlDB	INT		
HiAlDB	INT		

The only input variable that changes continuously over time is the engineering value of the measured quantity EngValue while all the other variables are fixed parameters. The value of EngValue is supplied by the iY variable of the previous UDFB block Conv4_20mA, which is in fact recalled by the main program immediately before AnalogSts.

The other 7 input variables are generally set either by the operator, by means of the HMI keypad, or by the programmer when coding a fixed value in the program source. We are going to see these variables one at a time.

The most important parameter is obviously the **SetPoint** and that is the desired value, set by the operator according to the operational needs of the system. It is always associated with a **Hysteresis** which determines the permitted oscillation band. Adding and subtracting from the SetPoint value the value of half of the hysteresis we can calculate two output variables: the high operating value **HighOper** and the low operating value **LowOper** that show the maximum and minimum oscillation limits tolerated. When the acquired value exceeds the high operating value, the subsequent control strategy will, for example, start a new machine, while when the acquired value will be lower than the low operating value, the control strategy will stop one of the machines already in motion.

The function block also includes two other values that can also be configured from the keypad; they are the HighAlarm alarm and the LowAlarm alarm. The high alarm must be set to a value higher than the operating value, while the low alarm must be set to a value lower than the low operating value. When the measured variable exceeds the high alarm value, it means that the control action adopted with the high operative is not sufficient and therefore a more energetic action is required for the control strategy by starting two or more machines instead of just one. Similarly, the strategy will have to stop more than one machine if the low alarm is passed downwards.

The function block uses two even more external values; they are the HighReas high and low LowReas reasonableness limit. Normally these are coded in the source by the programmer. For example, if the inlet pressure sensor operates in the 0-25 bar range, any value below -1 bar or above 26 is an unreasonable value, synonymous with faulty probe. This value can not therefore be taken into consideration by the subsequent control strategy, while the alarm chain must intervene, which must alert the operator to analyze the cause of the fault and eventually replace the sensor.

The last input parameter to be analyzed is the DeadBand. This parameter is necessary to avoid oscillations in the output status caused by electrical disturbances that cause the measured value to oscillate slightly. In the absence of a dead band if the measured variable is close to an operating or alarm limit, there is a risk of continually starting a new machine or in any case seeing the status fluctuate between the values "within limits" and "operating high". By programming a small deadband value, commensurate with the predictable disturbances, the developer can stabilize the control chain.

Let's now analyze the output variables. The most important is AnalogSts, hence the name of the functional block. It is an integer variable used as a basis for text strings associated with the status of the quantity to be regulated. We will then assign the encoding of the state of the controlled quantity to this variable, stored in the PLC register Status, and defined as text decoded from the table (Text Table Data) in the HMI device.

The AnalogSts function block uses the following instructions.

Rung R1 initially resets the sensor error flag, as shown in figure 4.7.2.

Rung R2 checks the condition of low reasonability and, if checked, sets the value 6 of the status and the sensor error flag. The function blocks used are the comparison between registers and the single copy function, both standard language function blocks, as shown in figure 4.7.2.

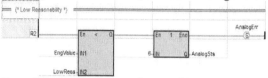

Rung R3 checks the condition of high reasonability and, if checked, sets the value 7 of the status and the sensor error flag, as shown in figure 4.7.3.

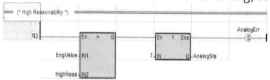

Rung R4 calculates the high and low operating values based on the SetPoint and hysteresis values using the standard sum and subtraction function blocks, as shown in figure 4.7.4.

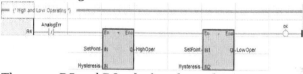

The rungs R5 and R6 calculate the analogous correct values derived from the application of the deadband, as shown in figure 4.7.5.

The R7 rung initially sets the status within the limits by setting the status to the value 1, as shown in figure 4.7.6.

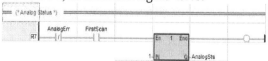

The rung R8 verifies the high alarm condition by setting, if checked, the status to the value 5, as shown in figure 4.7.7.

The rung R9 verifies the high operating condition by setting, if checked, the status to the value 3. The function block used in this case is the comparison block with the upper and lower limit values, as shown in figure 4.7.8.

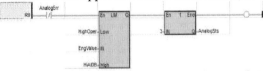

The rung R10 verifies the low operating condition by setting, if checked, the status to the value 2 as shown in figure 4.7.9.

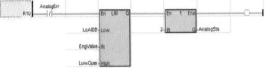

The rung R11 verifies the low alarm condition by setting, if checked, the status to the value 4 as shown in figure 4.7.10.

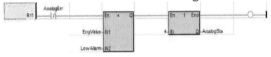

The rung R12 verifies the inlimits condition by setting, if checked, the status to the value 1 as shown in figure 4.7.11.

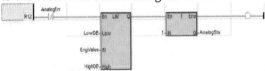

Finally, the R13 - R17 rungs set the output Boolean variables according to the value of the AnalogSts output variable. The function block used is the standard comparison for the equality condition, as shown in figure 4.7.12.

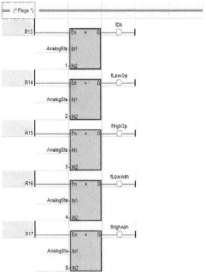

The presence of six Boolean output variables from the functional module will have been noticed. These variables will be used as "trigger" events by the specific sub-program that will have to operate the plant's machinery in sequence.

2.5 The AnalogSts Human Machine Interface

In the case in which the measured variable must also be regulated, we will define a new Numeric Data control, this time of the editable type.

The desired Set variable will be configured with the register that will contain the SetPoint input variable of the previously analyzed UDFB AnalogSts module, as shown as an example, in figure 3.18.1.

The Set variable has a Decimal format, an unmarked decimal, represented with two full digits and two decimal places, 12.12. The unit of measure is bar and it is possible to edit the value in a range between 0, corresponding to 0.00 bar, and 2500, corresponding to 25.00 bar.

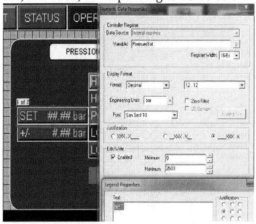

We also define the hysteresis which, as already mentioned, is the difference between the upper and lower switching values, which in our case are the desired values of APHighOp (9.00 bar) and APLowOp (7.00 bar), as shown in figure 3.18.2. In fact, we can, for convenience, define a PressureHyst variable that contains exactly half of the actual hysteresis value.

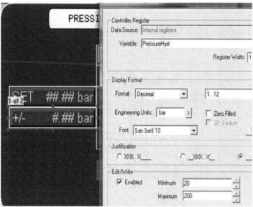

So if we set 8.00 bar as the desired value (set-point) and 1.00 bar as the +/- value (half of the hysteresis) we will obtain the desired operating values. In our example, +/- may vary between a minimum of 20 (0.20 bar) and a maximum of 200 (2.00 bar).

In the same way we proceed for the HiAlarm and LowAlarm registers.

The measured variable, as well as the calculated high and low operating limit values, are defined as non-editable, as shown in figure 3.18.3:

Finally, we will assign the encoding of the state of the controlled quantity to the AnalogStatus output variable of the function block, by defining the related decoding table 5 (Text Table Data) in the dialog shown in figure 3.18.4:

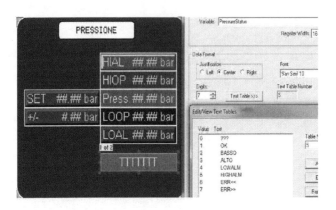

2.6 The VirtualAI subroutine

Problem

The VirtualAI subroutine is designed to meet two needs:
1) concentrate all the analog input signals in a single sub-program to facilitate visual debugging;
2) decouple the actual readings of the analog inputs or AI Modbus registers with the measured variables. The DebugAI flag is not used within the subroutine but in the main program call.

Solution

For each analogue input, the acquired value is copied to a global register. Figure 3.14.1 shows, in rungs R1-R2, the use of the copy function block of a single register from the variable AI1, related to the analog input wired to the level sensor, to the LevelRead registers associated with% R201 and PressureRead, associated with% R191.

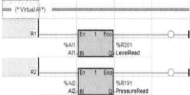

The following rungs operate in the same way with the analog inputs of the absorbed current sensors of the set of pumps as shown in figure 3.14.2.

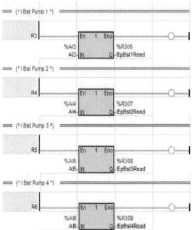

The recall from the main program

Rung R7 of the main program invokes VirtualAi as long as the DebugAI variable is not set, as shown in figure 3.14.3.

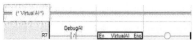

By setting the temporary DebugAI flag to 1, the process of copying the analog inputs to the process registers is interrupted. These can therefore be "forced" by the programmer to test the correct operation of the program by means of a development PC or by a special HMI mask.

At the end of the test the developer will reset the DebugAI flag which, however, for each First Scan, is reset, for security reasons, from the R5 line of the main program.

2.7 The Init subroutine

Problem

In a real application we usually use the Login subroutine that allows us to implement the management of Viewer, Operator, Service and Vendor roles characterized by increasing levels of authority.

Each of these roles are allowed to access specific HMI screens. The first application start-up passwords are initialized by the program using the Init block. Subsequently the user with privileges of SERVICE or VENDOR can reconfigure them from HMI keypad.

The subroutine is also used to set default values for the initialization of relevant application registers.

Solution

Rungs R1, R2 and R3 set initial arbitrary values if they find that the corresponding registers contain null values, as shown in figure 2.7.1.

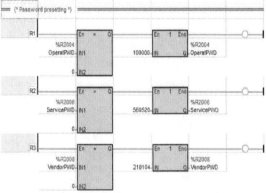

The variables that define the working fields of the 4-20mA transmitters, also need to be initialized, as shown in figure 2.7.2.

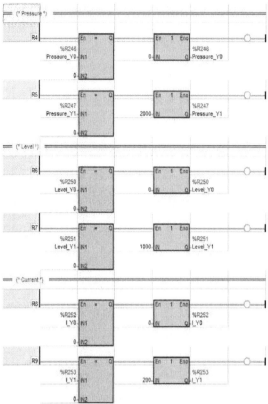

The initialization of the alarm timer set follows, as shown in figure 2.7.3.

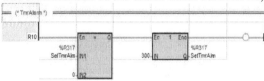

The call from the main program

Line R1 of the main program invokes Init unconditionally, as shown in figure 2.7.4.

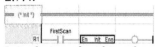

It is obvious that this subroutine having to provide default values to the others must be the first to be recalled in the main program.

3.1 Water level measurement and control logics

The example shown is taken from my book "PLC - HMI per Stazioni di sollevamento acque reflue e meteoriche" of the book series AUTOMAZIONE DEGLI IMPIANTI TECNOLOGICI awaiting translation into English.

Logical Development

a) First of all we proceed to the implementation of the measurement of the level in the tank. Let's start by creating a LevelConv object as an instance of the UDFB Conv4_20mA function block, described in chap.3.3. We know that 2 PLC 16-bit registers are required: the first in input to accommodate the register of the reading to be converted; the second output to memorize the engineering value of the level. We will associate the% R201 and% R202 registers of the Plc to the global variables LevelRead and LevelValue. The latter will provide us with the measurement of the level in the tank.

b) We create the function block UDFB Conv4_20mA with the logic instructions shown in chapter 3.3.

c) We define a specific subroutine LevelMeter which, as the first instruction, will call the Conv4_20mA function block through the LevelConv instance, as shown in figure 3.1.1:

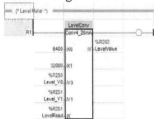

The next rung is required for the final Demo of the application developed in the aforementioned book.

Since we hypothesize to use a level sensor with range 0 - 10.0 m, the values of iY0 and iY1 have been set respectively to 0 and 1000 (10 m with two decimal places) while the values of iX0 and iX1 being native channels are placed at 6400 and 32000 respectively (0 - 32000 or 0 - 32767 if you plan to use different PLC hardware).

c) The subsequent development involves the implementation of control over the acquired level. In this regard, we will create an instance of the UDFB AnalogSts block, already described in chapter 2.4. We know that nine PLC 16-bit registers are needed plus a certain number of Boolean variables. Then we proceed to define the required variables.

The non-retentive global variables used are shown in figure 3.1.2:

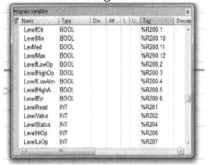

while the retentive ones are 4, as shown in figure 3.1.3:

editable by the operator on the HMI keypad.

d) We create the UDFB AnalogSts function block with the logical instructions shown in chapter 2.4.

e) In the LevelMeter subroutine we add the call of the LevelCtrl instance of the AnalogSts function block, as shown in figure 3.1.4:

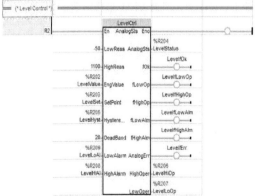

The LevelMeter subroutine is now complete.

f) We must however associate the LevelRead input variable with an analog input. For this purpose, we create the standard VirtualAI subroutine, already illustrated in chap. 3.7, to group all the definitions of the analog input channels. At the moment we only have one for which the subroutine will have only one instruction, as shown in figure 3.1.5:

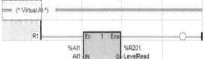

We will associate the Boolean variable DebugAI to the temporary bit %T8 of the PLC. In Debugging mode we will set this variable to 1 so we can force LevelRead to the value we want regardless of the value of the first analog input AI1.

g) Now we just have to add the calls of these two subroutines in the main main program, as shown in figure 3.1.6:

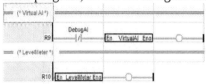

Monitoring is thus implemented.

3.2 Water level measurement and control HMI

The SYSTEM screen offers a synoptic representation of the pumping system whose automation is described in the previously cited book. The visualization of the level control is shown in figure 3.2.1.

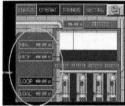

The left side highlighted by the yellow elliptical outline displays, in Numeric Data graphic objects, the values of the operating and level alarm limits. The value of the level and its state are shown in the upper part above the tank, as shown in figure 3.2.2.

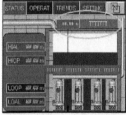

A specific graphic control allows to dynamically visualize the water level, as shown in figure 3.2.3.

This is a new type of Bar / Meter control that is configured quite simply by indicating both the measured variable LevelValue and the minimum and maximum values that it can reach, 0-1000 in our case, corresponding to the engineering values of 0.00 -10.00 m, as shown in figure 3.2.4.

To set the level sensor adjustment parameters dynamically, the SETTING screen is used, as shown in figure 3.2.5:

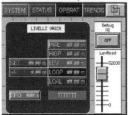

In the blue frame the SET, +/-, HIAL, LOAL values and the duration of the interdiction period are set.

On the right side two tools useful for the test: the AI debug switch and the LevRead slider that allow us to simulate the reading of the analogue input, as shown in figure 3.2.6.

Now let's see some real shots obtained during the test phase in the pumping system automation application described in the book from which the example is taken.

With the slider we start to simulate the actual level to see if the statuses of the level meter are correctly displayed.

We start from the condition of level 0.00 m which corresponds to the status of Low Alarm, as shown in figure 3.2.7.

We increase the level with the slider up to 2.44 m corresponding to the Low Operating state, (BASSO in Italian) as shown in figure 3.2.8.

The level is then increased with the slider up to 4.03 m corresponding to the state Ok, as shown in figure 3.2.9.

Finally we increase the level with the slider up to bring us to 4.67 m corresponding to the High Operating state corresponding to the HIGH text (ALTO in Italian), as shown in figure 3.2.10.

Raising the slider to values close to 32000 will show the status of HIGHALM.

3.3 Pumps sequencer logic

As a next step, we show how the outgoing flags from the AnalogSts function block can be used to implement the functionality related to the sequential start / stop of submersible pumps. If the level exceeds the HIOP value, an available pump will be started. On the other hand, if the level falls below LOOP, one of the active pumps will stop.

The consecutive start / stop will be implemented based on a preset delay "T Station" variable, set on the operator panel, that we will store in the EpSewSeqSet retentive variable associated with the register %R302.

If the level were to exceed the HIAL level, all active pumps would be immediately started and an alarm signal would be generated. If the level falls below the LOAL level all the active pumps would be immediately stopped and an alarm signal would be generated too.

In addition to the control strategy under normal conditions, must be also envisaged the cyclical alternation of the pumps in order to standardize the wear and the automatic substitution of the pump, locked due to failure, with the first pump available.

Parallel Sequencer

To implement the above specifications we will use the design pattern related to the Mot6Seq parallel sequencer that will be illustrated in the third booklet of this series.

a) We insert the call of the Mot6Seq block as a starting line in a specific SewagePumps subroutine, defining the retentive variable EpSewSeqSet, associated to register %R302, as the input parameter setInterdition and the global variable EpSewSeqWord, associated to register% R301, as the output parameter wordSeq, as shown in figure 3.3.1.

```
                EpfSewOn                          SewSeqPump                        Ep1SewOe
         R1 ─────┤ ├─────────────────  EpOn1  WofkSeq  oEpGo1  ───────────────────────( )──────

                     Ep2SewOn                 EpOn2    oEpGo2         Ep2SewGo
                ─────┤ ├─────────                                  ───( )───
                     Ep3SewOn                 EpOn3    oEpGo3         Ep3SewGo
                ─────┤ ├─────────                                  ───( )───
                     Ep4SewOn                 EpOn4    oEpGo4         Ep4SewGo
                ─────┤ ├─────────                                  ───( )───
                     AlwOff                   EpOn5    oEpGo5            ok
                ─────┤ ├─────────                                  ───( )───
                     AlwOff                   EpOn6    oEpGo6            ok
                ─────┤ ├─────────                                  ───( )───
                   Ep1SewReady                                         %R301
                ─────┤ ├─────────  EpRdy1   wordSeq  EpSewSeqWord
                   Ep2SewReady                                      oSewSeqintrerd
                ─────┤ ├─────────  EpRdy2   oSeqintord  ───────────────
                   Ep3SewReady
                ─────┤ ├─────────  EpRdy3
                   Ep4SewReady
                ─────┤ ├─────────  EpRdy4
                     AlwOff
                ─────┤ ├─────────  EpRdy5
                     AlwOff
                ─────┤ ├─────────  EpRdy6
                   Ep1SewFback
                ─────┤ ├─────────  EpFblok1
                   Ep2SewFback
                ─────┤ ├─────────  EpFblok2
                   Ep3SewFback
                ─────┤ ├─────────  EpFblok3
                   Ep4SewFback
                ─────┤ ├─────────  EpFblok4
                     AlwOff
                ─────┤ ├─────────  EpFblok5
                     AlwOff
                ─────┤ ├─────────  EpFblok6
                   LevelHighAlm
                ─────┤ ├─────────  iHiAl
                   LevelLowAlm
                ─────┤ ├─────────  iLoAl
                   LevelHighOp
                ─────┤ ├─────────  iHiOp
                   LevelLowOp
                ─────┤ ├─────────  iLoOp

                                           NrPmp
                     AlwOn
                ─────┤ ├─────────  Start
                       %R302
                 EpSewSeqSel  sadnterditon
```

The output flags coming from the AnalogSts function block become the input flags iHiAl, iLoAl, iHiOp, and iLoOP of the sequencer block. The subroutine generates the Go flags for the number of pumps provided in the NrPmp input parameter.

The logic continues normally with the recalls of the ElectricMotor blocks treated exhaustively in the first booklet of this series.

As we can see, the functionality related to the sequential start / stop of the submersible pumps has been obtained using only the functional blocks described in the present series without the need to develop additional user logics.

3.4 Pumps sequencer HMI

The sequencer display can be obtained with the STATUS screen, which summarizes the operating status, the local commands as well as the Go command variable Go of each pump; also adding the information status from the sequencer, as shown in Figure 3.4.1.

4. Summary

We have reached the end of our second booklet. I would like to thank the reader for the effort made to read it and for the trust given to me as the author.

I am sure that the result achieved will be fully positive and that the quality of the future work carried out, by implementing the techniques acquired, will emerge with sufficient clarity and will be a source of great professional satisfaction.

A sincere wish of good work and a goodbye to the next booklet that will deal with the sequencers.

Made in United States
Troutdale, OR
05/01/2024

19575626R00027